Hi Jax,
Have Fun
chee

D1231527

26

Things That Bug Me

By Mike Raupp

With drawings by
Jeff Kollins

Barclay Bryan Press

Printed in the United States of America.

Barclay Bryan Press, Inc.
PO Box 409
Port Republic, Maryland 20676
www.barclaybryan.com

ISBN 978-0-57804526-9

CPSIA facility code: BP 305600

To George, Hilda, Ivan, Deak, Hank, and Bon for telling me stories.

To Michael, Erin, Brian, and Paula for listening to my stories.

To Tina, Linda, Ethel, and Sheri for bringing out this story.

To Patty, Dan, Jessica, Tara, Mehmet, Kojo, Diane, Charlie, Robin, Chris, Bill, Howard, Sam, Liz, George, and Tisha, who seem to like six-legged creatures and helped me share bug stories with so many people.

Hello!

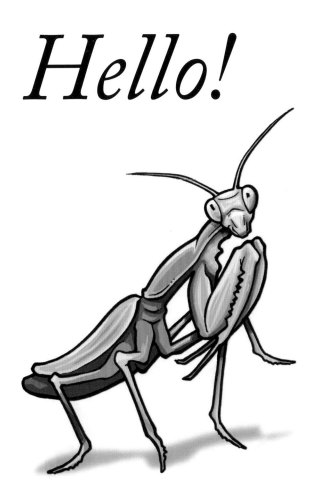

My name is Mantie, and how do you do?
I'd like to practice some letters with you!
Just turn the pages and look carefully.
If you are lucky, you might just find me!

is for Antlion

The antlion sits in a deep, sandy pit.
She catches small bugs tumbling
down inside it.
Small ants, tiny beetles, she finds
them all yummy!
A snippity snap, and they're safe in
her tummy.

B

is for
Bumblebee.

T he bumble bee bumbles from
flower to flower,
Sipping sweet nectar
in each waking hour.
The nectar and pollen go straight
to her hive
To feed her bee babies and
keep them alive.

C is for Cicada.

For seventeen years,
they are not to be found.
They are sucking on plant roots
down deep underground!
To the treetops they fly
after waiting so long,
And they sing to each other
their strange noisy song.

D

is for Dragonfly.

Dragonflies dance
in the blue summer skies,
With powerful wings
and enormous great eyes.
They swoop through the air
catching bugs on the wing
And eat while they zoom.
They are cool.
That's their thing.

E

is for Earwig.

The earwig, my dear,
is nothing to fear.
Despite what you've heard,
it won't climb in your ear.
Those pinchers you see
at the end of its tail
Are for picking up groceries,
garbage, and mail.

F is for
Firefly.

Fireflies are great bugs
    to catch in a jar
On a dark summer night,
    when they blink like a star.
If you catch one, remember,
    you should set it free.
They must eat, rest, and play
    just like you and like me.

G

is for Green Lacewing.

L ook closely – these lacewings are
    beautiful things,
With shiny green eyes and delicate wings.
But small lacewing youngsters do not give
    out hugs!
They are hungry meat eaters and eat other
    bugs.

H is for

Hickory Horned Devil.

The horns on this devil are easy to see
     As it gobbles the leaves of a hickory tree.
This big caterpillar should cause you no fear.
It becomes a large moth in less than a year.

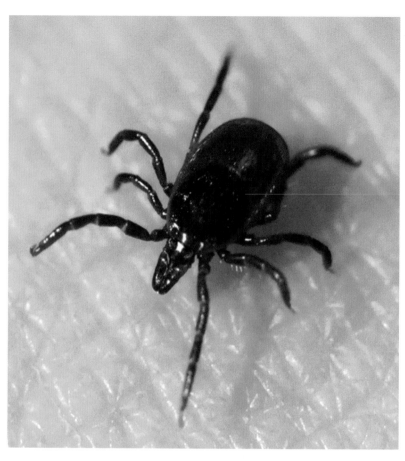

I is for Ixodes.

L ook out for ixodes – black-legged tick.
If this one should bite you, it could
make you sick.
When you come inside, carefully look all
about.
If you find any ticks, pick them off, toss them
out.

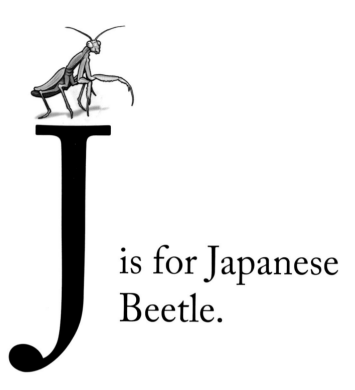

J

is for Japanese Beetle.

These beetles will feast in the month of July.
You see them on plants where they run,
walk, and fly.
They like to eat roses and all kinds of leaves.
Their babies, called grubs, munch on
roots as they please.

K

is for Katydid.

*K**aty did, Katy didn't* is what these
      bugs say.
The guys sing at night but not during
      the day.
They make their weird bug songs by
      rubbing their wings.
They hear with their legs! Oh my!
      What strange things!

L is for Ladybug.

These ladies are good bugs to have
on your plants.
They eat pesty bugs. They don't give
them a chance.
So, bad bugs, watch out! You'd better
be ready,
Or you'll disappear like a plate of
spaghetti.

M

s for Monarch Butterfly.

The monarch is queen of the butterfly clan.
  When young, she eats milkweeds. It's part
     of her plan.
The fall is the season she favors the best.
She flies to the south for some sun
        and a rest.

N is for Nymph.

Nymph is the name for a very young bug.
If they were way big, you could give them a hug.
As nymphs grow and change, they do very strange things –
Like turn into grownups with two pairs of wings.

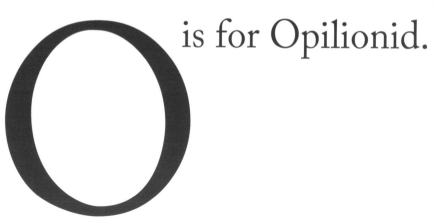

is for Opilionid.

You might know these critters as
   "Daddy Long-legs."
The dads don't do much, but the moms
   lay the eggs.
With plenty of legs they stroll all
   through the land,
And make awful smells with their
   stinky stink gland.

P is for Praying Mantid.

Oh, I am fantastic at catching my prey!
Cricket is on the lunch menu today.
Two spiny legs help me capture my food.
(I eat the head first to avoid being rude.)

is for Queen Butterfly.

The queen butterfly has some
    tricky surprises.
She basks in the sun just as soon
        as it rises,
And if the birds catch her, she has
        a good trick:
One taste of her blood makes them
        throw up! How sick!

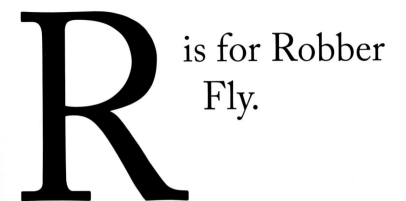

R is for Robber Fly.

The robber fly's face is remarkably hairy.
To many small bugs he looks really quite scary!
When no one is watching, this robber will pounce
And eat tiny bugs by the gram or the ounce.

S is for Saddleback Caterpillar.

The saddleback dresses in brown and light
    green.
But don't let that fool you, this babe can
    be mean!
The spiny spines found on her head and
    her tail
Sting badly enough to make grownup
    men wail.

T is for
Tiger Beetle.

This tiger can't growl. He can't snarl, yell, or roar.
But he runs, jumps, and hides on the dark forest floor.
If you're hoping to catch him, you better be quick
And have a big net on a bug-catching stick.

U is for
Unicorn
Beetle.

Unicorn beetles have really great horns!
They look just like crazy enormous-
sized thorns.
The boy beetles use them for fighting,
you see.
They battle for places to live in a tree.

V is for Velvet Ant.

Do *not* let the velvet ant get in your
pants!
If she does, you'll be dancing the
velvet ant dance.
She can give you a sting. She can give
you a bite.
You will hop, skip, and jump on one leg
half the night!

W is for Wheel Bug.

The wheel bug is wearing big spokes on her back.
She moves *v e r y   s l o w* as she plans an attack!
The large beak you see in between her front legs
Is for poking and eating small bugs and their eggs.

X is for Xylocopa Bee

Xylocopa is really a carpenter bee.
The work of the mom is quite
    something to see.
Her jaws carve a perfectly round hole
    in wood
To serve as a home for her babes.
She is good!

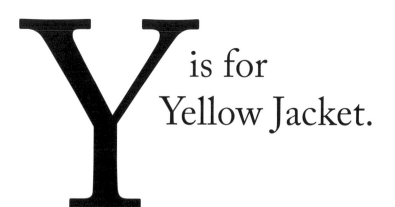

Y is for
Yellow Jacket.

This fierce fancy lady is easy to see.
    Her cheek is bright yellow and so is
        her knee.
She lives with her mom in a papery nest.
Applesauce is one of the foods she likes
        best.

Z is for Zebra Butterfly.

How did this butterfly get its cool name?
It looks like a zebra!
The stripes are the same.
If you want to know where this
mom's babies might be,
Just look on the leaves of the strange
paw paw tree.

Wasn't it fun meeting my friends and me?
Did you learn every bug, and each ABC?
If not, have no worries, for here's a good plan:
Just open your book up and read it again.

When you finish, be sure to jump up, run,
    and play.
Go outside. Look for lots of cool bugs right
    away.
Learn all of their names, and observe what
    they do –
And see if some bugs are like me and like you.

So long! For now, Mantie bids you adieu.
Next time we meet, I'll bring more friends for
    you.

Mantie and The Author

The End